Contents

Stuck on a dune
Focus on: u_e, ue as in *cube*, *blue* 3

A day at the zoo
Focus on: oo as in *moon* 5

The Hat Man's new roof
Focus on: ew, **ew** as in *few*, *grew* 14

Phonemes: ch, sh, th, wh, ph, a_e, ai, ay, e_e, ea, ee, y *as e*, i_e, ie, igh, y *as i,* o_e, oa, ow, u_e, ue, oo, ew

'Tricky' words: my, can't, does, love, here, are, look, our, eyes, house

About this book

These short stories are designed to give children blending and reading practice. They are decodable, which means the words in them only include letter shapes and sounds that the children have learned. The stories gradually introduce 'tricky' words, building on the learning in the Red Series.

The progression links directly to the teaching order in the Letterland teaching range. Each story begins with a title page that provides important information for children and teachers.

Story title

Focus on: New spelling patterns introduced

New 'tricky' words: Common words with irregular spellings

Basic teaching tips:

- Encourage the sounding out of decodable words (and any decodable parts of 'tricky' words).
- Discuss the stories with the children to ensure comprehension and engagement.
- Encourage re-reading in pairs or individually to develop fluency and reading for meaning.

Red Series introduces the a-z letters and sounds and some 'tricky' words'. On completion of this series, the following words remain tricky in part: **a, the, she, oh, for, that, ok, they, says, her, this, to, said, of, what, you, was, want, come, sees, asks, do.** These words are included in **Blue Series**.

Stuck on a dune

Focus on: u_e, ue
as in *cube, blue*

On a dune, Sue plays a tune on her flute.
A cute cub peeps from a blue tube. He can't see Sue playing her flute so he jumps up on to the huge dune. The sand is soft and the cub sinks in to the sand. He is stuck. The sand is like glue!

"You are cute!" says Sue. "Let me rescue you!"

A day at the zoo

Note: Young readers may require help with the words **penguin** and **zookeeper** which are only partly decodable.

Focus on: oo as in *m<u>oo</u>n*

We went on a school trip to the zoo. We went in a blue bus. It was a hot, hot day.

We soon got to the zoo. Then we had to choose what to see. We went to the cool side of the zoo, the penguin pool!

There were grown-up penguins and cute, fuzzy, baby penguins.

They had rocks by the pool with snow – at least I think it was snow. They even had an igloo!

We pretended to be penguins. It was funny. They are quite slow on land but sometimes they hop. We did that, too.

At noon, the zookeeper in boots came with a bucket of fish. He threw the food in the pool.

The penguins zoomed in the pool. Woo hoo! Splosh!

In a big window we looked at the penguins swim. They had lots of room. The penguins had smooth coats.

Just then, the Zookeeper yelled, "Oops!"

By mistake, the zookeeper had let ten penguins loose. They had set off to see the kangaroos.

He chased most of them back to the pool. But a baby penguin was still loose.

"I know what to do!" said Aboo.

He pretended to be a penguin and the baby penguin began to follow him! Slowly it followed Aboo back to the pool.

A zookeeper scooped up the baby and put it back in the pool. The children and grown-ups thanked Aboo for his fantastic baby penguin rescue!

The Hat Man's new roof

Tricky word: house

Focus on: ew, ew as in *few*, *grew*

Did you know that the Hat Man has a house with a hat on top? But his house used to have a roof. Until...

On a bright spring day, the Hat Man was at home making hats. He put on the news.

The news said a big gale was on its way. They said, "Close the windows and stay inside."

So he did. As the sky grew black he sat inside his home. He chewed on a roll and ate stew. He knew his horse, Henry, was safe inside his hut, right next to the house.

A few raindrops splashed on his windows. He knew the gale was on its way.

It began to rain and rain. The wind began to blow. It blew the leaves off the trees. The gale grew and grew.

Then..., the wind blew the roof right off the Hat Man's house!

It threw the roof up and then blew it away! The Hat Man ran from his house to the hut to check on his horse, Henry.

Henry was chewing on some hay. His hut was fine!

"Phew!" the Hat Man said to Henry.

So the Hat Man and Henry waited in the snug, dry hut for the gale to end.

But then the Hat Man needed a new roof.
"I know," he said. "I will make a big hat and use that as a roof!"

He drew a plan for a new hat roof!

He made that big, green hat so it would not blow away in the gales. Then a crew came to help him screw it on top of his house.

And that is the tale of the Hat Man's new roof.

About this series

This series of 10 books accompanies the Letterland teaching range. Each book contains a selection of short stories. In total there are 32 engaging stories featuring the phonic elements listed below as well as some 'tricky' high-frequency words.

Book	Focus elements	As in the word...	Story titles
1	sh, ch, th, th, wh, ph	<u>ch</u>ip, <u>sh</u>op, <u>th</u>at, <u>th</u>ing	Check on the chicks Shep and me What is that thing?
2	a_e, ai, ay	m<u>a</u>k<u>e</u>, r<u>ai</u>n, s<u>ay</u>,	A safe place Kate bakes a cake Kane's tail!
3	e_e, ea, ee, y	th<u>e</u>s<u>e</u>, s<u>ea</u>, b<u>ee</u>, bab<u>y</u>	A trip to the sea Mr E's trees Happy!
4	i_e, ie, igh, y	l<u>i</u>k<u>e</u>, t<u>ie</u>, n<u>igh</u>t, m<u>y</u>	Ben rides his bike Cats at night What a mess!
5	o_e, oa, ow	h<u>o</u>m<u>e</u>, b<u>oa</u>t, sh<u>ow</u>	The bad goat When the cold wind blows Lost in the Queen's maze
6	u_e, ue, oo, ew	c<u>u</u>b<u>e</u>, bl<u>ue</u>, m<u>oo</u>n, f<u>ew</u>, gr<u>ew</u>	Stuck on a dune A day at the zoo The Hat Man's new roof
7	ar, or, er, ir, ur, wr	f<u>ar</u>m, f<u>or</u>, h<u>er</u>, g<u>ir</u>l, f<u>ur</u>, <u>wr</u>ite	The big match Snapshots The bird girls My very bad morning
8	o, oo, u, oy, oi	s<u>o</u>n, b<u>oo</u>k, p<u>u</u>t, b<u>oy</u>, c<u>oi</u>n	Oscar's brother The big pull Nick's noisy new toy
9	aw, au, ow, ou	s<u>aw</u>, c<u>au</u>se, h<u>ow</u>, <u>ou</u>t,	Draw it! The house mouse Look now!
10	Review ear, air	p<u>ear</u>, y<u>ear</u>, f<u>air</u>	My shark dream A fresh feast Bears at the fair A fairy story

Collect the sets

Phonics Readers - Red Series

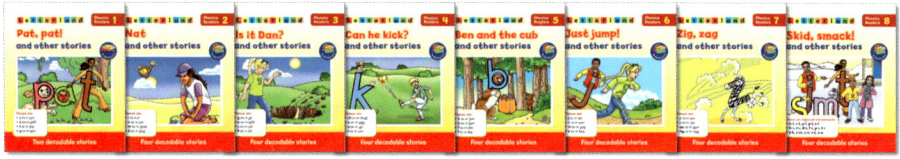

Phonics Readers - Blue Series

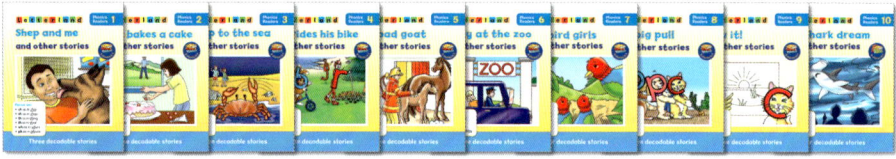

Published by Letterland International Ltd. 8/10 South Street, Epsom, Surrey, KT18 7PF, UK.
www.letterland.com
ISBN: 978-1-78248-185-0
Product Code: TJ07

© Letterland International 2016
LETTERLAND™ is a trademark of Letterland International Ltd.

First published 2013. This new edition published 2016.
Reprinted 2023.
10 9 8 7 6 5 4 3 2

Authors: Stamey Carter and Lisa Holt
Originator of Letterland: Lyn Wendon
Artwork: Baz Rowell and Doreen Shaw
Design: Lisa Holt

The author asserts the moral right to be identified as the author of this work. All rights reserved. No part of this publication may be reproduced, stored in a retrieval system, or transmitted in any form or by any means, electronic, mechanical, photocopying, recording or otherwise, without either the prior permission of the Publisher or a licence permitting restricted copying in the United Kingdom issued by the Copyright Licensing Agency Ltd, 90 Tottenham Court Road, London W1T 4LP. This book is sold subject to the condition that it shall not be by way of trade or otherwise be lent, hired out or otherwise circulated without the Publisher's prior consent.

Printed in Beirut, Lebanon.